Special Thanks

We would like to thank God first and foremost for what he has done for us and how he has provided in our lives each and every day. Secondly, to our loving wifes and our children for their support and encouragement. Also, for all the people close to us that gave encouragement as well, we thank you all.

GOD BLESS!

O'Donis is coming to town to check on his 10 bee hives. He wants to make sure all of them are keeping the honey flowing!

Before O'Donis makes his grand visit, his 10 retail bee hive stores will market all the honey they have made.

HONEY !!!
HONEY! SALE!
CLOSED
HONEY! HONEY!
HONEY! SALE
HONEY!! SALE ★
SWEET HONEY
CLOSED
HONEY! HONEY!
CLOSED
SWEET ★ HONEY!
SALE! HERE!
HONEY!

One day, the bee hive manager held a meeting with all the bee hive department heads and told them that the big corporate bee, O'Donis, was coming to visit hives 10, 2, and 3.

This is bee hive number

ten!

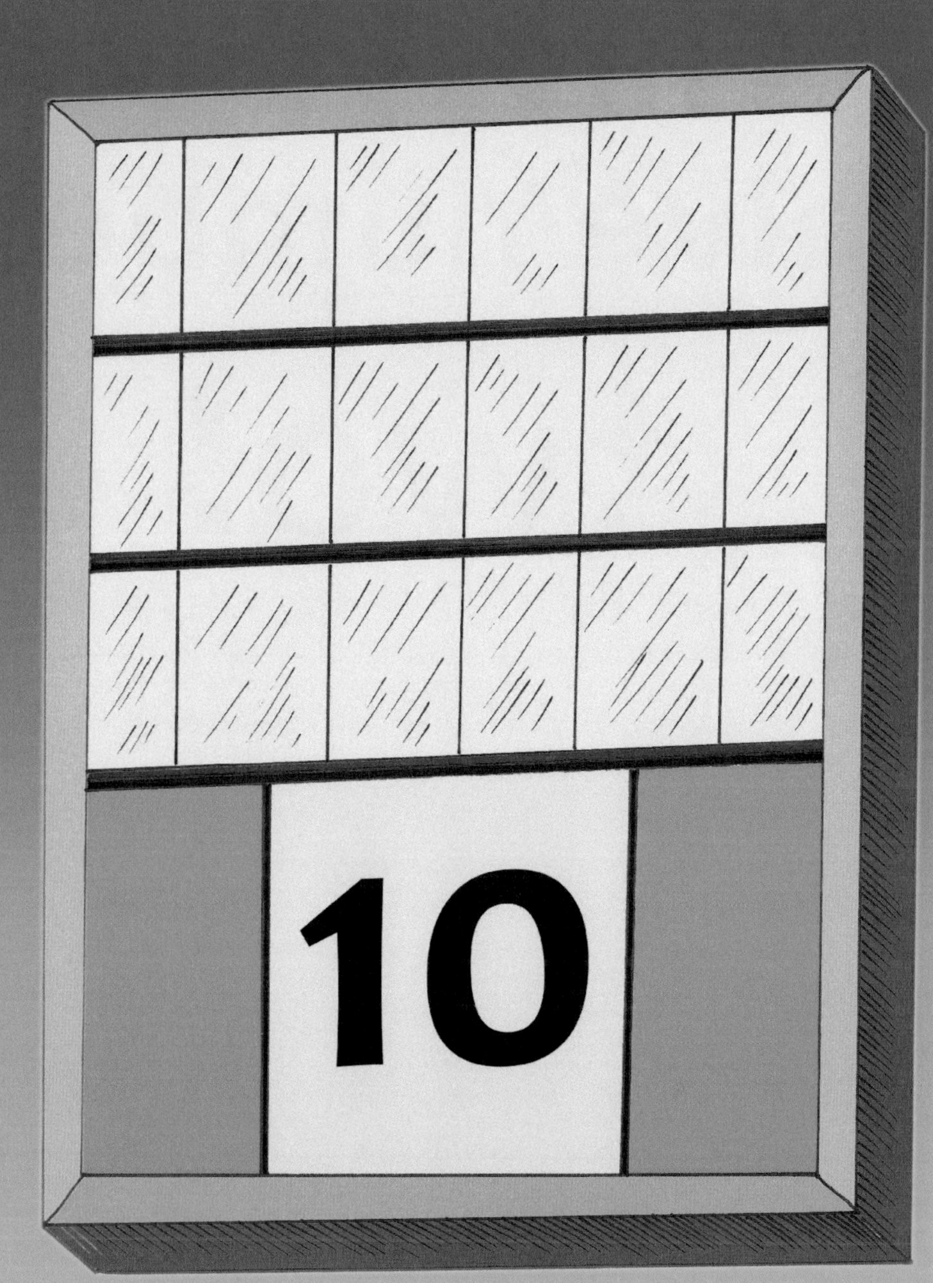
10

This is bee hive number

two!

2

This is bee hive number

three!

3

So, the worker bees scurried around doing extra work to ensure that their hives were in the best condition before O'Donis, the corporate bee, came to town.

The day comes and the day goes; O'Donis, the corporate bee, never shows.

IS HE EVER COMING?

Once again, they received the word;

"O'Donis is coming,

O'Donis is coming!"

The seasons come and go, and O'Donis, the corporate bee, never shows.

The worker bees are exhausted but don't let their guard down. Because one day, they know O'Donis will come to town.

The End!

ALWAYS
BEE
WATCHING;
BECAUSE
JESUS IS
COMING
SOON!

Book Written by: Brian Paschall
Illustrated by: Derek Dalton
Cover design by: Derek Dalton
Book designed by: {Brian Paschall} and {Derek Dalton}

 Life event humar packed inside a child's story book.

Dreamed up and Printed in the {United States of America}
{Derek Dalton} {Brian K. Paschall}

Made in the USA
Coppell, TX
19 January 2024